Hodder & Stoughton
LONDON SYDNEY AUCKLAND

In association with
Peabody Trust

the big issue

book of home

compiled & edited by Eddie Ephraums

First published in Great Britain in 2000, by The Big Issue, 236-240
Pentonville Road, London, N1 9JY and Hodder & Stoughton,
A Division of Hodder Headline Ltd, 338 Euston Road, London, NW1 3BH.

10 9 8 7 6 5 4 3 2 1

British Library Cataloguing in Publication Data.
A record for this book is available from the British Library.
ISBN 0 340 75657 8

Packaged for The Big Issue and Hodder & Stoughton by Eddie Ephraums.

Originated by Primary Colours, Chiswick, London – 020 8995 8402

Printed in Spain by Imago.

home unites us all

Home unites us all. We've all had one in the past, even if we don't have the privilege of living in one at the present. We all have an image of what home should be like and an expectation of what feelings our ideal home should instil in us – even those who haven't got one. Some of us who have one feel 'homeless' inside ourselves – restless and incomplete. Others, without one, say that the comradeship of their fellow travellers, with their worlds of experience, provides them with a 'home', however transitory it may seem.

This book brings together people from all walks of life around a common theme – 'what does home mean?' *Big Issue* vendors, homeless people, readers of the magazine, students of photography and aspiring young photographers create the words and images that pose and answer the question.

The Big Issue Book of Home is also significant in that it proves there is power in creative expression and that we can all access this power, however 'privileged' or 'disadvantaged' we are. For this reason we have not identified which contributors are homeless: the quality of the work speaks for itself.

The Big Issue is proud to be associated with the *Book of Home*. We have worked with thousands of homeless people over the years and we have always had a profound belief in their potential. This book, too, is about believing in potential. It has provided writers and photographers with the opportunity to take the next step and, just like *The Big Issue*, it has empowered people and given them a greater belief in themselves.

Lucie Russell
Chief Executive, The Big Issue Foundation

Home is more than a place to sleep and put your things. It gives you somewhere to spend time with your family and friends (or escape from everyone else!). It offers you security and the freedom to do what you want to do, a place to unwind. Home is the anchor point in a busy life, a rock in a world of relentless demands, opportunities and change.

Without a home, living the life you choose is hard, if not impossible. For the thousands of families and single people in Britain who live in temporary housing, bed and breakfast accommodation and are sleeping rough on the streets, not having a home is much more than not having a permanent roof over their heads.

This is why *Peabody*'s work as one of the largest providers of housing for former rough sleepers in London embraces much more than bricks and mortar. We provide practical help with essentials such as furniture, give advice on benefits and employment, run training schemes and offer additional support for those with particular needs like care leavers and those with substance misuse problems.

Creating long-term stability is also the reason why *Peabody* (in partnership with *Centrepoint*) set up *Safe in the City*, an independent charity that tackles the roots of youth homelessness. Through mentoring, training, peer support and family mediation, *Safe in the City* aims to prevent young people from becoming homeless in the first place through targeted early intervention.

This book is a glimpse into what home means for different individuals. It's also a reminder of what it means not to have one.

Richard McCarthy
Chief Executive, Peabody Trust

finding home

I passed him one day as I walked to the pool. Without thinking, I stopped and paid a pound for the magazine, then carried on. I had never bought a copy of *The Big Issue* before. I don't even remember if I smiled at the vendor or said hello. I was preoccupied with a book I had just read; it was a beachcomber's intriguing story about his personal journey home. I was wondering where such a person could be found in London.

It was at the tideless swimming pool that I stumbled upon the answer. Didn't the vendor stand in the same place every day, watching the ebb and flow of life? I went back to his pitch.

'Hello,' I said, 'I bought a copy from you earlier.'
He smiled; perhaps he had heard this a hundred times before or was it that I had stopped to speak with him? We chatted for some time and agreed to meet again.

Of course I asked him about home and he replied by showing me a tattoo. *Made in Aldershot* was inscribed around his navel. Then Simon told me the name of the little hospital where he was born. Did I know the place? It was my birthplace too. But what of home now?

He was homeless.

At this time I was living in a campervan, exploring life without a conventional home, and while our situations were clearly different, we agreed they too shared a common background – the belief that they were part of a home journey. But what about other people's views of home? Simon suggested that I meet *The Big Issue*'s Writing Groups and ask them.

What they wrote inspired this book. And just like the beachcomber's story, or Simon on his pitch, *The Big Issue Book of Home* is an invitation to discover where we all stand.

Without finding this, what is home?

Eddie Ephraums

Right: **Eddie Ephraums** and **Simon Hart**

When I first met Simon, *The Big Issue* vendor who helped to initiate this book, his home was a garage where slugs roamed.
At night the place was pitch black. Once he woke to something finger-like brushing his cheek and 'was frightened like a child.'
But where was the reassuring light?

After the garage, Simon's home was an old ambulance in one of London's most expensive squares:
'It had the smallest lawn, but everyone could enjoy it.'

home

Every day, people make choices based on the fact that they have a home, anything from 'Shall I move?' to 'Should I stay for another drink or go home now?' The structure such choices provide suggests that home is part of a natural order. It's always been said that you can never go home again. I choose to believe that means the concept of 'home' evolves right along with you. It shifts from something physical to something spiritual.

When I was a child, home was a fixed point. It was where my folks lived. It was what I went back to every day after school. I ate there and slept there, in a room with my two older sisters. Some nights, we'd sit in the dark while they spun stories. The shaft of light from the street outside illuminated a thousand fantasies. Even now, a sunbeam through shadows or the glow of a projector in a darkened movie theatre will send me spinning back in time to a tiny bedroom in Littlehampton.

In order to grow, that home became something I had to leave. That's when the clichés started. While I was roughing it around the world, home really was wherever I laid my hat. Later, when I began spending all my time on the road as the face of a rapidly expanding international business, there was no place like home to come back to. And now, with the family growing and a handful of grandchildren to liven up the joint, home is where the heart is.

All the clichés add up to another, grander homily. Home is a state of mind. In the best of all worlds, home is the nurturing place where mind harmonises with body and soul. But we know this isn't the best of all worlds. So we have homelessness as an inescapable symbol of disharmony. The fact that the situation has arisen in the first place as a side-effect of the failure of various governments to make social responsibility an integral part of policy turns homelessness into an even more disturbing inkling of chaos. And that chaos is no abstract anarchy. It's the spiritual dislocation of thousands of lives cut loose from the choices, the structure, the succour of home. They're a swingeing penalty for progress.

It's past time to think about home as a human right.

Anita Roddick, OBE
Founder & Co-Chair
The Body Shop International

Right: **Richard Lewis**

nobody home

I envy people who moved around a lot when they were children; their memories, for good or ill, are scattered to the winds. Or people with siblings; all those shared memories, easing the burden. But I only knew one home, from birth until I broke away at the age of seventeen, and now that home is empty and both my parents dead, I and it are the sole repository of my family's brief shining moment of happiness, our collective day in the sun.

The house – a fifties semi in a working-class area of Bristol – looks so beautiful to me now, the embodiment of my parents' devotion to me and each other, a concrete expression of their steadfastness. But from the age of twelve to my departure, all I wanted to do was burn it down. (Within twenty four hours of my mother's death, I had managed to flood the kitchen through the bathroom floor, and was forced to pierce a hole in the kitchen ceiling so that it didn't collapse. It took my parents fifty years to build that house up, and me a day to start destroying it.) Though a slender and graceful teenager, beneficiary of many years of ballet classes, the house always seemed to me too small for three people, even though it had three bedrooms and a big garden at the back. Bigger families managed perfectly well in smaller houses; what was the problem?

The problem was me; my impatience and ambition and ego. From the moment I could walk, all I wanted to do was to run as far away from my parents as I could. Every time I moved, it seemed, I sent ornaments crashing with my ricocheting restlessness. Now everything in the house that I hated, that summed up the small life I wanted no part of, mocks me; the china clowns, the coloured brandy glasses, the unlikely pastel pups and kittens – well, you got what you wanted, they say, you'll never have to sit down to dinner here again. You can go anywhere you want. Now, of course, all I wanted is them, there.

The tragedy of hormones is that from the moment they kick in, we are compelled to seek out people like us. What we don't realise is that, if we are lucky, our parents are the people the most like us that we will ever find. All else is merely shadow-play, a trick of the light, which can be broken up by the merest flicker of a seven-year itch. Once a runaway, always a runaway; I would go on to create two homes, building them up with the utmost love and attention, then suddenly look around and see myself as a stranger, who must flee quickly to avoid detection.

I am very happy where I am now, and more in love that I have ever been. I live by the sea, which I always wanted to do; I have a beautiful house with fruit trees and koi and a swimming pool, just what I always wanted. And I know that one day I will take a wrong turning, realize this and keep walking away, until I am lost. Then, and only then, will I have come home.

Julie Burchill

Right: **Arran Elvidge**

As I walk around

As I walk around this town,
city-soon-to-be,
I look at various homes, and play
a game with me!
In my imagination, I walk up to 'my'
Door,
I rearrange the furniture, 'they' don't
live there any more.
I sit inside their gardens, swinging
on their swing,
And give away their furniture and
all that sort of thing.
I also look for places for
homes to be,
Spaces in 'their' places for a home for me.
It's alright, it's just a game, my little
Fantasy.
Still, one day, check your garden
the squatter there'll be me!

Rainbows Leeanne

Home?

– Nah.
Just some blank pages
where I wander
searching
– My pad.

Pamela

A place within everyone

Some people are still looking for the key, some have access only once a year, others have daily visits. Once you've found the key you'll never let it go.

Your home is filled with whatever is or was true in your environment, in yourself. It's that part of your soul that protects your contentment. It can be shared with whoever you let in. For me it's where my soul sighs in relief, shrugging off the hardships of the day, the disappointments of life. Doesn't care if there is no Oscar on the mantelpiece, doesn't matter if there's no mobile phone on my coffee table. There is no judgement and it's sweet.

Vanessa Bissessur

London

The outskirts are the far reaches of the garden,
that I occasionally visit
the centre is the kitchen,
where I do all my living.

People are what make my home,
all the millions that make their lives
but each wakes from a different bed,
some made for them with a warm duvet, some not.

Routines, of which there are many,
cross the tapestry of the sofa material,
different colours, different patterns,
differences.

Doors can't be locked to everything,
experiences are varied,
tinted glass can't prevent from seeing,
Diversity and Individuality.

Kate Appleby

Love

Home to me is where I am
Some days I'm in a building
Some days I'm not,
To have love in my heart
And a smile, that's home to me
It's where I want to be, you see!

Kev Lippiait

Home within

Home is
sometimes
a place
inside of me.

Misé

Another place

The word home does not
resonate with me
the nearest I get to it
is the sound of ôm.

Gerry Sean

A house

You can't sell me
What I already have.

Take your rose-covered cottage
Your lace curtains
Embroidered wisdoms
And plastic dreams.

A footprint
Is deep enough to have walls:

This is where I put my name.
This is where I sign.

Christina Park

Be a home

Be a home
where love is
Be a home
that houses all that is beautiful and real
Be a home
where everything in it is loved and cared for
Be a home
where the only disharmony is the soft aching to want
to house everyone who doesn't yet feel where home is
Be a home
where love is
at home.

Len Ball

Home (iii)

Where love changed to hate
playful rivalry became jealousy
where movements were restricted
every action looked on with suspicion
and privacy ceased to exist
where visitors were unwelcome
a familial totalitarian state
the home.

Charlie H.

What is home?

A box of bricks with a slate lid on it,
Wattle and daub villages on stilts.

Lush Amazonian forests, tepees,
Canvas and poles in a field.

Assorted cardboard boxes,
Covered in dirty tarpaulin.

A caravanette, car park stairs,
Anyway, who really cares,
When they rush home from work!

Martin

Times past
William Marshall

Times present
William Marshall

Picture perfect

It's the box house with its four square walls, that you drew as a child. A blue line of sky that doesn't quite meet the earth, a white gap left between heaven and ground; the sun is always shining. It's the white picket fence that never was; was a wall, a hedge, a stream, stone, brick, privet, fir, border boundary. It's the set-square door, bright pillar-post-box red with brass lion's head firmly biting down on a round ring knocker. It's the chequer-board windows: white wood crossed and uniform, with their B-bowed curtains, polka-dot patterned on polychrome colours. It's the little details of the few bricks, that make the house that Jack built. It's the single plume of moody grey smoke across a sunny sky; from the log-wood-coal fire that's always lit on winter days and cool evenings, roaring in an open hearth; which was central heating, electric, gas. It's the red tiles that fill the straight line outline of the upside down flower-pot roof; suggested, drawn or non-existent.

It's the garden with the green-grown fresh-mown grass. It's the flowers which barely balance on their line-thin stalks, looped leaves of fleshy green at the base, floral fantasies of six petals at the top, turning their friendly faces to greet the viewer. It's the trees, cotton-wool fluff on a chocolate trunk; green paint-textured splodges with red round apples, crisp crunch of juice on a summer's day, all year-round fruitfulness.

It's the rainfall, hail-storm, wind-gale, sunburn, snow-fall, on autumn days, spring, summer, winter. It's the snowman with the carrot clichéd nose, coal eyes and pipe-stuck mouth, the hat and scarf, more warmly wrapped than the cold-chapped child with bright burning cheeks. It's the paddling pool, water-wet and child-cold, cries of quick delight and longer undelight.

It's the place you carry in your heart. The place that will always be a part of you, wherever you are, the one which is at the back of your mind, the bottom of your cupboard and the centre of your heart. It is your home.

Victoria Elliott

A different place

There was once a keen-eyed builder, who found a lovely field. The grass was long and seedy, and in the hot sun butterflies danced and chestnut horses flicked their tails. Here and there stood ageing trees – though most got cut down the minute the farmer, who knew a good deal when he saw one, decided to sell the land. Before you could say 'Stop!', ten red-brick houses sprang up, and on Sundays happy young couples pulled on their boots and planted new trees, and flowers, and bags and bags of grass. In a few years you could barely believe that this world of lawns and babies in hats could ever have been a field.

One of the houses was different from the rest, because on its neat front lawn stood the last remaining tree – a big, pink-candled chestnut that tossed in the wind like waves. The small girl whose bedroom was next to the tree loved it for being old. From the top, she thought, you could probably see the sea.

The little girl was always rather shy. She had a mum, who gardened, and a dad, who went to work, and a brother who did things with Airfix and rushed around on a bike. She thought she had a friend or two but never dared knock on their doors. So often she sat in her room, making cardboard boxes into cosy miniature homes, with real green wallpaper and real velvet sofas and chairs.

Then one night, when she'd gone to sleep, she was suddenly woken up. She thought she heard a shout. Odd – but there it was again. And again.

Years passed, the tree got taller and so did she. And the shouting at night got worse, till it burst out into the day. The little girl, who was now not a girl at all, sat in her room and read. No friends came – she couldn't risk having them round. And no one guessed. Because apart from the tree there was nothing to show that her house was different from the rest.

In the end, her mum left and her dad stayed. He loved the house, but didn't much care about cutting or pruning, or housework or DIY. When the girl came back to visit she couldn't believe her eyes, because these days anyone could see that her home was the odd one out. In the neat road of low Sunday hedges, now one garden had green walls thirty feet high. The silver birches had flown up to meet the birds, the apple trees were wild, the roses had gone quite mad – they'd grown so tall you could pick a bunch from the bathroom window upstairs. And what had once been a lawn now wasn't a lawn at all. It was a field. A lovely field of long grass.

'Look at the butterflies,' said her dad. 'Just look how many we've got!'

Anna Lewis

Where life begins
Jane Dixon Halsall and **Andy Halliwell**

Home is being known
Lorraine Walshe

Lost and found

I feel I am turning into a snail
I take my home with me wherever I go
A little pack of memories sitting on my shoulders
Of a time when a house existed – solid and safe
Of a time when two boys with black tousled hair played
And I tried to ignore the emptiness in my soul.

Of a man who came and said 'trust me'
'I will care for you and them – all will be well'
And I did and followed like a disciple
This tall man
Who led us away from our home
To a dark place of shadows
And then left us.

Of a time when I sent my sons away
To a place I thought they would be safe
Because I knew I had nothing more to give them at that time
And began a journey of wandering
And I wander still in mind and body
And I listen to the voice inside that says
'The way you have chosen is unsafe and untrodden and you have no choice but to follow.'

And today my sons are with me
And their tousled hair still gleams in the early morning sun
As I watch them sleep and devour their gentle breathing
For tomorrow they will leave me
And return to their other life
I cannot follow
But will pack up the memories of these days together in my mind
And put them in my shell
To carry everywhere with me
I hope they know I take them with me in my heart
Wherever I am.

Jane A. Norman

Dead calm

Dead calm,
stands the plant
in my room,
my room.

A room of my own,
no one to see
who I am,
what I want to be.

The curtains are closed,
the lights are off,
light another ciggy,
cough another cough.
Put the light back on
so I can see,
off it goes again,
no one here but me.

Oh well,
the quiet will do me good,
now I know nothing else ever could.

Claire

A bachelor's room
Anna Ledin

A youth hostel room
Eva Edsjo

Home

The whole room was light as the sun,
he couldn't see beyond. He could hear alright.
Well almost, considering how loud it was playing,
'The Latest News Reports'
'Lahore & Calcutta in ruins'
'Russia near complete occupation of Iraq & Kuwait'
'Queen Mother in hospital with suspected Influenza'
'Troops attack demonstrators in Beijing, 38 dead'
'Israel launches nuclear attack on Baghdad & Teheran'
'Dollar collapses'
'Royal families now at secret locations'
'No news from Clinton & Blair'
'Martial law declared in 27 countries'
'Yeltsin reportedly dead'
'China occupies Japan'
'Nick Cotton to return to *EastEnders*'
'Yeovil Town beat Man Utd 7-0'

The solar bright light and all the terrible world
events only lasted an infinitely small fraction of
time during which he and his Home ceased to exist.

Pat

The view from my house's cosy bed!

I hide from the world under my cosy warm duvet,
Forget all of life's troubles and what I mean to say.

I stay quiet and warm, I sort of hibernate,
Forget the outside world and that I feel irate!

I forget shop doorways where I once froze at night:
Forget I had nothin', not even a shite!

Because these days I can hide underneath my roof,
Pass by the homeless, I guess I'm somewhat aloof.

But I always swore that I'd not end up like this,
I try not to think because I'm taking the piss.

Now, when I go out I always pass beggars by,
They ask me for spare change but I ignore their cry.

I feel so bad inside that I ignore my guilt,
And just carry on hiding under my quilt.

Martin

Round and round the garden
Jo Pitson

Home comforts
Amanda Rylands

Ship of dreams

Candles melting into the walls
thro' the posters, the wallpaper, the scented
spirals moving up and across the quickly
darkening room.

Movement and music become one
like the sky and ocean where the
horizon cannot be seen, then the
warrior ships appear and disappear
into the wide open grey blackness
of the ocean.

White water constant and revolving
loud and sometimes silent, rushing
the old harbour walls, crawling
creeping between rocks and beach pebbles
moving into the land.

The redundant ironmongers, red
brown rust, dented and spray painted
old skeleton fishing boats, green
slopes to the dirty muddy sea
the gravel wall and windowless
harbour-master's house.

The glue-sniffers and junkies shooting
gallery, the place of lost dreams and
romantic embraces, lost virginity
in many ways.

It roars like a thousand lions in anger
smash bang crack, the storms of winter
the sea-birds fly into the countryside
wet damp, wind-battered signs swing
creak and sing, wishing us to come into
the sorrowful plastic seated café.

The electric trains flash blue/white
overhead cables dance with rain and sea-water,
faraway dogs bark at some mighty unknown being
or maybe they bark just to get back
into their master's home.

The dog's master is most likely in
the horse-shoe shaped bar on the corner
shouting about whose dog or woman
or football team is or are the best.
Alcohol and idiots don't blend well.
The café is not very welcoming at all
but its calor gas heater with its limited
glow brings an unhomely warmth.

The other two customers are mid-teen
girls, not really dressed for this weather
out to get impregnated by some foolish
small town thug, they laugh at me.

The waitress knows me from a time before,
she asks the usual routine questions.
I find out she's never married and has two kids
and the council lawn, dreams of the time of her youth
(as I do).

The records jump and are two decades
old but you don't mind that, order a
coffee, fumble with fingerless gloves, fags
and lighters, damp matches, a song from
the seventies comes loud across the near
empty café.

Brings back memories of watching *Reservoir Dogs*,
and a smile and a flash of teeth appears on the face
of the teenage vixens,
I smile to smooth her modesty,
the calor gas fire pulls me to its blue yellow glow.

Nearing closing time, I order chips to take
home, but I've no home anymore, the salt
breeze shocks me and the town hall clock
still doesn't move on any of its four sides.
I head for the harbour and the shelter
of a boat, under the damp wood I sit
and think, sleep.

The dawn will be soon and I'll be
gone on my ship of dreams.

Steph

My home

I live in the yuppiest part of town.
Bustling Islington.
In Upper Street,
The constant flow of strangers in local restaurants and
wine bars.

Three floors up.
My view of the Angel, spectacular.
Every morning I greet humdrum rows of red brick family flats,
old orange chimney pots, black neat railings, a one way
street frequented by too many mad motor cyclists and fast
cars. A few remote trees, satellite dishes to catch all
those evening 'soaps' and the new Sadler's Wells, a thick
block of grey, vague, blossoming in true Brit style, waving
the Union Jack above the nearby red chimney pots.

Inside a familiar council block,
my flat is a riot of Caribbean colour,
two lazy worn yellow armchairs lounge in front of the TV,
a constant warm fire, stacks of multi-coloured files and
magazines, collections of everything from buttons to bric
a brac, every shelf and corner bulges. My bedroom leans
to one side accommodating all my junk and dreams with quiet
dignity.

No blessing of a house warming. My flat too compact to
crack open the best vintage champagne.

In my day dreams I drift to paradise on my bamboo raft,
smelling the fragrance of exotic flowers along the way.

Jeanette Ju-Pierre

Past caring
Alexandra Murphy

The calm before the storm
Tay Benedict

Home is where?

Home is where the hurt is,
The smacks, screams and 'don't do thats',
Dictatorial lectures,
Daily whacks,
The sly looks,
And slinky adult hands,
Shame on you,
Hussy slag,
Where you must eat all your food,
Or be force fed,
Beaten every morning,
For a nightly wetted bed,
Indoctrinated into bowed headed ugliness,
Father fearful he knows best,
Home is where the hurt is,
At least that's what all the homeless,
I have met have said.

Fee Jane

What am I?

Frilly curtains
Garden gnomes
Royal Doulton
Ideal Homes
Deep-pile carpets
Sunday tea
Triple glazing
That's not me.

Laughing children
Purring cats
Dressing up in
Silly hats
Dirty faces
Climbing trees
Understanding
This is me.

Jacqui Ford

A world without walls
Carolyn Watts

Home is where the hearth is
Peter Mallett

Heating my home

Living in a non-heated home
the cold fills the house
all year round
winter brings the horrors
of its cold, bitter, blows
waking to worry from the constant pressures
reminded of the same old routine
you can see bodies lose their heat in a mist of steam
aching limbs begin to click
and the cold air holds breath
the only comfort comes from
each other's own warmth
rubbing our numb fingers and toes
where will the heat come from next
unable to move from our stale bed
moving and shivering
goose bump-like skin
trying to keep the cold air from getting in.

Lucy Newman

You are my home

Home is my street
where I can be fed
by the warmth of people
no matter how good or bad they are.

Home is my little patch
to talk to you sometimes
or when you talk to me
not to feel isolated.

Home is where we walk together
to feed our spirits.

Home is not a home
if you are neglecting me
all the time.

My home
is divided into a million hearts
and where a house is not a home, for without your love
I will die.

Fabiola Ruiz

Seven sisters.
Moreen, Liz (Ethel), Pearl, Iris, Bernadette (Mavis), Yvonne and Lorraine.
Gina Turner

Objects and pictures fill given spaces
In this space we love and we ache, we laugh and we cry
It's hard to look at certain things and it's hard to feel
Houses we inhabit, in homes we live
Mark Le Ruez

Merry go round

Plink! The dying sob of a light bulb plunged the room into darkness. Dave closed his eyes. He'd been getting too tired to read anyway. He'd just read the same paragraph three, nearly four, times and still didn't have a clue what was in it. Come to think of it he couldn't remember the last couple of pages. It was definitely time to sleep. He turned on his side and pulled the sleeping bag over his long lanky frame. Then he had to readjust the jacket that he was using as a pillow, then he had to pull up the sleeping bag again.

The room was icy-cold. Its solid concrete floor was directly over the basement car park allowing cold air currents to suck away any warmth the economy central-heating might produce. Dave had put a couple of layers of cardboard down as a mattress. It was only a temporary measure. He'd catch his death of cold if he relied on that thin carpet for insulation. He'd have a real mattress soon. People were always throwing them away. He'd just have to hope to come across one on a dry day.

Dave's mouth was really dry. He hadn't slept in a centrally heated building for years. He was used to going without things, and under normal circumstances he'd have managed without. Having a tap, two taps, only metres away changed things. He was nice and snug now. If he got up for water he'd only have to get comfy again. His thirst and the novelty of having running water so close to hand got the better of him in the end.

It was fifteen days before he found a mattress. Funny how you can never find anything when you want it. He'd added a couple more layers of cardboard by then and he'd managed to blag a couple of really nice pure wool blankets from the handout on account of a purely imaginary allergy. Someone else had given him their old electric kettle, and he'd found a toasted-sandwich-maker in a skip that had only needed a fuse. He'd also blagged some tea-bags and coffee which he and his pal Tommo were drinking from polystyrene cups from the Issue office.

'Thanks for helping with the mattress mate.'

'It was a pleasure man,' replied the dark, dread-locked little man. 'What goes round comes around.'

'So what d'you think of the place?' Dave asked.

Tommo had to consider the matter for some time before replying. 'It's very square and ... I dunno ... clinical. Yeah that's it, it. It reminds me of a hospital.'

Dave had to agree, but as soon as he got his grant off the social he'd get a few posters and wall-hangings to cover up those bare white walls. 'And I'm going to get a cooker, and a fridge, and a TV and a stereo, and a big lump of hash.' They sat quietly for a while before Tommo broke the silence.

'I dunno mate. I can see the advantages of having light at the touch of a button and hot and cold running water at the turn of a tap, but I just find all this concrete so oppressive. Call me trailer scum if you like. Call me a hippy, but I feel the electricity buzzing through the walls and I could never put up with the noise your plumbing makes. Talking of plumbing d'you really think it's hygienic to shit in the same hole all the time? I'm convinced it's healthier to go in the bushes and dig a fresh hole every time and cover it up and put it back into the earth than it is to flush it away.' Tommo stood up and pulled aside the dirty grey blanket that served as a curtain over Dave's only window. 'Look at that view. A bit of concrete and a few wrought iron railings, and on the other side of the concrete a building identical to the one you're living in. Yeah I've parked up between buildings before and had worse views than this, but at least I've been able to hitch up my trailer and go look for a better view. I've seen what happens to people when they don't get on with their neighbours in these concrete-rabbit-hutches. You end up looking through the peephole before you open the door just to avoid bumping into them in the corridor. These places turn people into cowards. Cowards or psychopaths. Wasn't you just telling me there's been two cars burnt out underneath your flat since you moved in, and didn't you say there was a dead junkie found in the bins the other day? No way I could share my front door with no one.'

It was another three days before Dave found himself looking through the peephole before going out. It wasn't that he was afraid of the bloke across the corridor. Hell, he'd sorted him out good and proper. Hah, he weren't afraid of him. He just didn't want to see him outside his own front door. Shit, it was just like being in prison. A free man should be able to choose his neighbours! Why couldn't he have his own front door?

He'd laid awake all that night. His grant was due in the morning. He was about to get the biggest wedge he'd had in three years. He'd be able to make this place real cosy. It'd be so good having a cooker and a fridge, and a TV and video. It wasn't just anticipation that had kept him awake. There'd been a fire in the block opposite. Some old alkie had died apparently. It was ages before the fuss died down. Then the plumbing had kept him awake. He'd been awake when the first light of the dawn had emerged around the edges of the dirty grey blanket. He'd been awake as the post came through the letterbox. The sound of a fairly hefty envelope hitting the mat was all it took to send him to sleep.

He woke around three thirty. He was up and dressed and out the door in seconds. Halfway to the post office he'd realised he'd left his ID behind. By the time he'd gone home, found his ID, lost his keys, then found them again, he'd had to sprint to the post office. He'd made it but only just. By then it was too late to do any shopping, except at the off-licence. He'd had to walk past three offies to get home. He'd managed to resist the temptation. Making do with a pint of milk from the last shop so's he could celebrate with a cuppa.

Dave was just putting his coat on to go out and look for some hash when the buzzer went. It was Tommo on the blag. 'Dave mate you've gotta help me.' Tommo was getting evicted in the morning and needed to borrow a tenner for diesel. 'Honestly mate I've had it up to here. My missus is in maternity having a baby and not one of them hippies will spare a bit of diesel so's I can move me trailer. If I had a flat to move into I'd give me whole rig away. I'm fed up of having to fetch and carry things like wood and water. Me missus should have her council place soon, but I can't be bothered to wait. I ain't even got gas at the moment and I won't be able to get any till payday.' Dave got on with making the tea whilst Tommo carried on bemoaning his fate. He knew what he should be spending his grant on but seven hundred quid could pay for a good holiday. As he handed Tommo his tea he just had to ask.
'How much is your rig worth?'
'I could get six hundred for the transit, but it's really only worth three and the trailer's worth a hundred and fifty, so I'd be well chuffed with four and a half for the lot.'
'I wanna go somewhere warm for the winter. I'm on the sick so me rent's going to get paid anyway. D'you reckon this flat's worth forty-five a week to you?' Tommo nodded, he'd already worked out what Dave was going to say next. 'So your rig would be worth ten weeks' rent. Might as well call that three months. That'd give your missus time to get her council place won't it, and who knows I may never come back, so you might have the place indefinitely.'

Twenty-four hours later Dave was driving his new rig off the ferry at Calais. He planned to drive to Brindisi in Italy. If he was lucky the hippy ferry would still be running, and he'd just about make it in time for the orange harvest in Crete or Cyprus or wherever it was.

Gary Brighton

Tinker's bubble
Sara Hannant

Alec Wallis

Castle of dreams

Security blanket I'm wrapped in bliss
Balm of morning hue
filtering through, softening the room
Layers of colour soothing my mind
Safely curled up in my castle of dreams
And protected from the waves of confusion
that invade my life.

Kate Drake

Wolverhampton ring road man

He lives on the edge of a deadly road
In a house of cloth and cardboard boxes
His only friends are the spluttering cars
The occasional bird and family foxes.

He once had a castle to call his own
A place of bricks and wood and mortar
A place that was stolen from him by fire
Along with his beautiful wife and daughter.

As he looks back on the life before
His castle is nowt but a burnt out shell
Never again can he call it home
He can only exist in his canvas cell.

Mocked and despised by the ones who suspect him
His dwelling place is an island of peace
It's as much of a home as he's likely to get
Alone with the nightmares that never cease.

Stuart Fenton

Prologue to 'The people I love'

When I think of home, the images that float through my mind are not those of painted walls and soft carpets, but of the people who live there. The people I love.

Home is the name I use to refer to the place where I find unconditional love from my family and where I give it in return, but it's also a feeling of giving and receiving.

The surroundings are unimportant, as is the rest of the world, when I'm with the people who mean more to me than anything else ever could and that feeling of comfort, of familiarity, of stability and, most importantly, of love, is what home feels like to me.

It's a simple word for a complex and beautiful feeling and I've expressed it in words (badly) as best as I could above and in the following poem.

The people I love

It can be the walls dividing physical space
Home looks like a loved one with a smile on their face
It's in the warmth of the fire and the dog on the rug
And the feeling of love when sharing a hug
The sensation of relief when coming through the front door
Talking to a friend for an hour or more
Home is a sanctum; floor below and ceiling above
But to me home is with the people I love.

Tracey Minutillo

My place
Rebecca Lewis

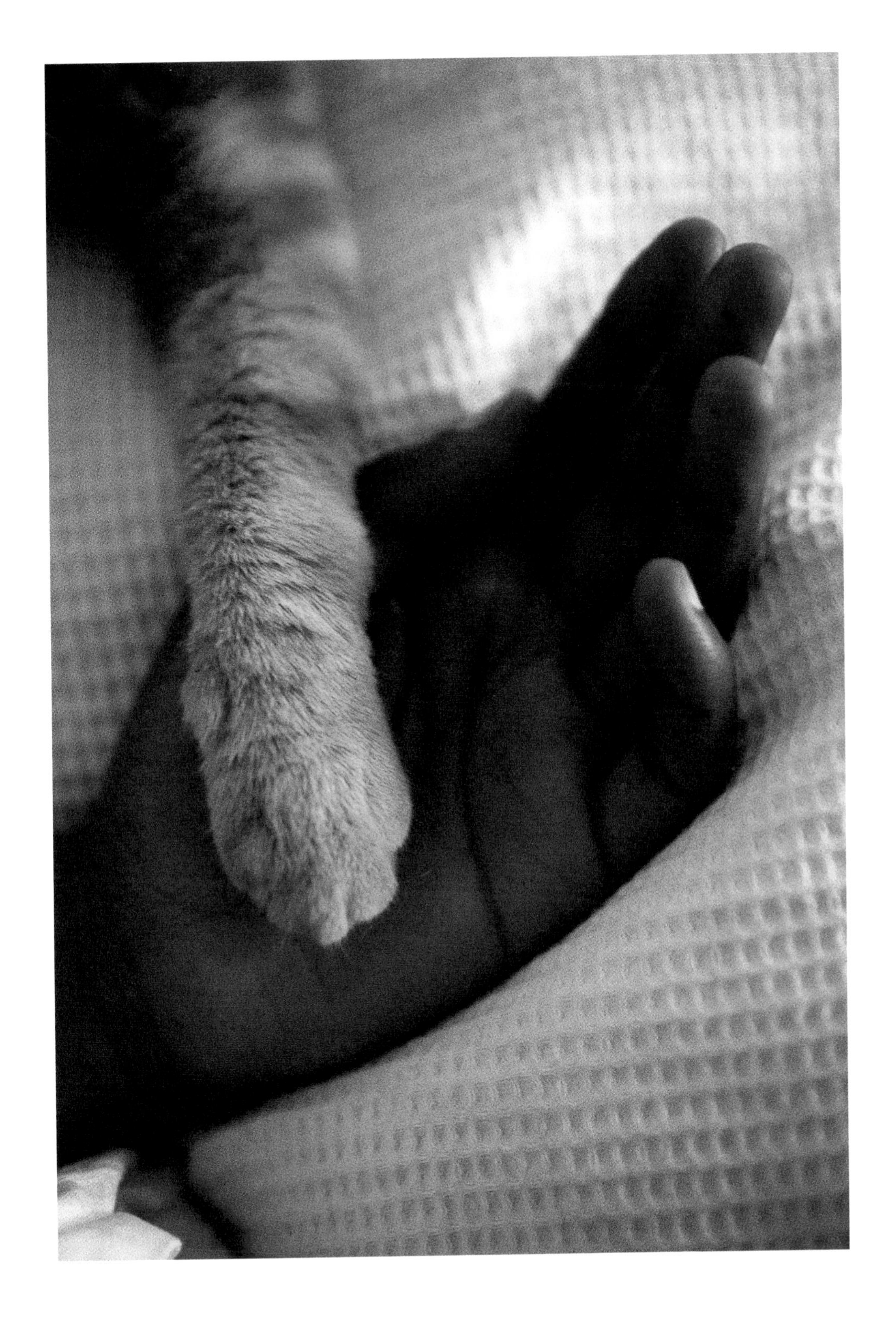

Hand in hand
Calina Zadrevetz

What is home?

What is a home to you?
Is it somewhere to lay your head?
Somewhere where you feel safe,
where you have your own bed.
What does a home consist of?
A roof, four walls and a front door?
Fitted carpets, armchairs and a sofa,
dining table and chairs and so much more.
Home to me it's a place you retreat to,
and leave the world's worries outside.
A place to build a comfortable nest,
and yeah, even sometimes hide.
It's a place that gives you shelter,
if you like, a safe port in a storm.
It's a place where you make your own rules,
and to nobody else's rules do you have to conform.
But to me I ain't got a building,
that I can call home.
I just make my home on the streets,
and wherever my feet take me and I roam.
My carpets are the tarmac and paving slabs,
and my armchair is often a wall,
but it doesn't bother me as I am a survivor,
and each day I always walk tall.

Tommy Joyce

Home is here

Borrowed shadows cast upon an
empty room, begin to rise.
As the sun unveils its presence.
A stranded breeze seeks solace
with my broken window-blind,
rattling out a merry tune.

The bustling sound of the coffee-maker
greeting me good-morning,
as its aroma envelopes my senses.
My mother busy milling around the kitchen
working to a set pattern,
a pattern developed over many years.

My father sitting at the weathered table,
his eyes searching the morning paper
for answers, but not knowing the questions.

Good and bad times forever etched
throughout these timbers
laughter and crying echoed in these
walls of life. Home.
Home is here.

Mark Mahon

Paved with gold
Tony Wong

Refugees
Running away from places, people.
These are nomadic times in life,
when nowhere feels like home.
Though they say there is no place like it,
it can be elusive.
Home is not four walls.
It is a feeling within.
Somewhere one feels comfortable.
Loving and loved.
Able to be oneself.
Natasha Kerr

Back home

They asked me where my home was
So I pointed to my back
And said 'I've everything I need right here
My life is in this sack.

'I have the freedom of the open road
The parks are mine at night
No mortgage hanging round my neck
No bills to cause a fright.

'My spirit cannot be contained
Within four walls of stone
I wander round the universe
I'm happy on my own.

'Yes home is where my brain is
Why on earth should I conform
To the narrow minded ideals
Of the scared who set the norm?'

Bernie Laprade

Moonlight marionettes

Midnight, see the moonlight marionettes' shadows on the ground,
piece by piece
home is lifted
furniture creaks as it is lifted silently, speedily, by moonlight marionettes.
Racing against time
back and forth, to and fro
'Faster! Leave it, we've got to go.'

Morning will bring the truth we fear
bailiffs and hammers to all we hold dear,
money we had, has all been spent
to eat, to live,
not for the rent.
Bricks and mortar versus hunger and thirst,
Peoples' needs must come first.
Time wasn't given to hear our plea,
the moonlight marionettes have had to flee
cutting their strings to their property.

Jacqueline-Anne Baker

A welcome home
Andrew Sanderson

Isolation
Annabel Baker

Museum of our lives

Home.
It was a lonely place after she went.
I threw her toothbrush away
and gave her clothes to charity.
Took our pictures off the wall
and wondered what to do next.
Now home was gone.

Fifteen years of home.
Fifteen years
packed up in cardboard boxes
wrapped up with string
and the heaviest heart.
Put them in an attic and tried to think
of something else but her.

But there were her socks
her tiny white cotton socks
and her lipstick
her brush – with her blonde hair still in it
her shoes, her wallet
things that made no sense
without her
things that hurt too much to throw away
and too much to keep.

I cried into her pillow
her blue and white striped pillow
which still smelt of her, still stained with her mascara
from when she was still just sleeping
and this was our home.

Sofas, chairs, tables, lamps
our living room now just a collection of furniture
a museum of our lives
of something that had been and ended
that would never be again.
How to understand never?

Home still exists in my mind
a lonely image now she's no longer around to sustain it.
Home was her – I know that now
back then we simply just shared it.

A childhood lost, a mother gone
got to try now to be my own home.

Kristin H. Sunde

The home love built

A fireplace, of what use is that in summertime?
And a patio's of no use when winter calls
A kitchen serves its purpose, 'cept when all are fast asleep
And a window's firmly shut as the rain falls.

Of what use is a bed without a mattress, a tub without a tap?
A toilet when too ill to get out of bed?
Your company is appliance after appliance,
toy above another toy
All serving wants but how about what we need instead?

What's the measure of a smile that greets you at dawn, worn
on a face you've come to love?
How much that voice reciting those three wondrous words?
How about acceptance and encouragement, goodwill and
fond farewells?
Are these things far too expensive for all to afford?

Oh what is a home without the laughter of loved ones that
surround?
Even if you've got Sky or digital TV?
What is a man who knows not hope, or has nothing to believe
To keep him going when all he sees is uncertainty?

Of what use is a garden to a man without a friend?
Of what use is a heater to one whose heart is cold?
How does an opening in the wall help one who has
refused to see?
Of what use is tomorrow for one still watching yesterday
unfold?

But there are things to serve you,
be you black, white, young or old
Widower, spinster, or having just been carried over the
threshold,
Something to serve you regardless of the situation faced
Something for both the coward and the bold.

It has a name, it is known as Love
And it is patient, sustaining pain without complaint,
It is kind even when wronged, doing good no matter what
And is one possessing remarkable restraint.

It is not envious, nor does it boast, and pride it is without
It's not afraid to say 'I'm sorry' or 'I love you,'
It's neither selfish nor rude, and is so slow to temper
Keeping a record of wrongs it is not known to do.

It hates the sight of any evil, rejoices in what's true
It protects, defends, it hopes and oh it trusts,
It is always persevering, and when true it never fails
And this kind of love for all homes is a must.

So plaster your walls with laughter,
to cover the silence around
Lay down a carpet of encouragement and not critique,
Spread humility over the bed, and truth to frame the doors
And let sincerity and forgiveness cushion each seat.

Let hope be the pane found in your window,
faithfulness your timber be
Let peace and joy be found in every room,
So tomorrow, whatever it may be, can be anticipated with a
smile upon each face
To me, you see, that is what makes a home.

Lanre Iroche

Somewhere to dream
Andreas Papandreou

With friends
Lesley Aggar

Edinburgh

I can't see that Brighton is ever going to feel like home to me. It's only home in that it stands within these wee islands. I'm dead fond of the place. Proud of it even. I'm always insistent that any folk visiting see at least one sunset down the beach and catch the starlings doing their thing at the West Pier. My younger sister came down, first visit, without meeting up with me to show her the place and left with an idea of a town full of old couples sitting in deckchairs waiting to die and the Palace Pier – 'FOR £1.00 ONLY. FUN.FUN.FUN.' The next time she came down a few good pubs, clubs and a wee bit of shopping for some of the hippy shite you can't get up the road changed her mind fair quickly.

Edinburgh, that's home. How anyone can not fall in love with Auld Reekie is beyond me. There's nowhere I'd rather have grown up. Nowhere. New York and London would come a poor second and third place but getting off the train from London gives me a buzz I can't describe (that makes me a pretty poor excuse for a writer eh?). But I know I'm home. Seeing the castle coming into the station ... I will admit that the castle is overrated. The collection of the most stunning buildings in any city centre in this country more than make up for it. Then there's being able to see The Firth from so many parts of the place. What more could you want for?

Maybe you're beginning to get the idea that I love my home town. It's not often I wax lyrical about anything, never mind bringing architecture into it. Some folks don't take to the smell of the breweries. You never do get used to it. Plenty of the residents get fair pissed off with the yearly intrusion (as they see it) of The Festival. I love it but it transforms the place for the last month of summer before winter kicks in hard and fast, leaving little space for autumn. Last time I was up home was for The Festival, and though I can hardly bring myself to say these words – I was almost a tourist. No - scrub that – the place is my home. My city. It always will be. But ... but I did see it from another angle this time round. We always either lived there or made a working visit? This time was pure time out. I could hardly take in what I was doing. I walked, strolled even, down Princes Street, not taking the back streets, not steaming on through elbowing my way past the uncountable number of rucksack-wearing photo-taking, bagpiper-watching pavement huggers. I didn't even get wound up about them, curse them once. I was chuffed for them to be seeing the beauty of my home town and as I took my time walking along the top of Princes Gardens and looked up at the castle I knew I'd been away from home too long.

Lisa

Home is a strange land

Home is a strange land, people do things differently there
I am moving away, but I don't know where
A new millennium should mean a new start
If not in my head, then in my heart.
Maybe I need to escape and run away
I close my eyes and it's night, even though it's day
I want to open my eyes, see what I'm running to
Who knows? Maybe to death, maybe to you

I'm leaving home, leaving it all behind
Looking to the future, looking to find
What? A new life? A new career?
Something I won't find by staying here.
I'm only young but I feel so old
From things I've seen, things I've been told
I have to move on, I have to be free
But am I scared – can you help me?

For one person home is heaven, for another it is hell
As for the difference, I probably couldn't tell
Maybe a home is where my heart is
Maybe home is where the party is
Maybe the questions will never be answered
Maybe no one is even bothered
And what if things aren't what they seem
And I wake up and home was just a dream

Maybe home is where to stay in after being out
But I feel at home when I'm out and about
Maybe home is four walls – does that make sense
But prison is four walls too so what's the difference?
Perhaps home is where memories are made
And prison is where hopes fade
So what if home is just a state of mind
Well then it cannot be defined.

Steven Kent

The fourteenth floor
'We bring them down here with some sandwiches and make a day of it. It gets the kids and us out.'
Tessa Bunney

'We're sick to death of this place being developed ... now we want something for us.'
Tessa Bunney

No one at home

You can tell by his stare that
There's nobody there.
Sitting alone waiting for the ring
Of the phone.
He's been pushed to the edge slowly
Losing his head
Finding no reason to get out of
Bed
Scritching and scratching till finally
He bled.

Nobody comes to visit him
They think he's turned into such
A bore
Going on about the weak, fragile,
Hungry and poor.
The rivers, seas, oceans and trees
He was so passionate about
These.
It's wrong, bad and drives you mad
This we agree is what they
Say
But let's have a beer and
Drink our troubles away.
He could never make them see
The pain that haunted him night and
Day.
Images of dying children that
Wouldn't go away.

Tried to make a difference so
He took direct action,
Got beaten and arrested trying
To stop the destruction.
Lost his job, his house, his lover
And also his conviction.

Now he sits alone waiting for
The ring of the telephone
Though it was disconnected months ago.
And you can tell by his stare
there's nobody there.

Peter

Apparently I'm homeless

I find this quite amusing as I do in fact own my own home. I'm the only member of my family who can say this. I can't help but respect my eldest brother who will own his place in less than twenty years, and my sister and her new husband who are about to sign themselves up to a similar long term bondage agreement. My home may have cost a lot less but I'm still proud of it. I quite like the idea of having wheels on my home as well. When I get bored with the view I can go and find a better one.

People ask how I live without electricity. They seem quite shocked when I tell them I have gas to cook on. They seem equally shocked that I can live without TV. I don't need a TV when I've got a wood burner which is much more fun to look at, and I can play with it. It's freezing cold outside I can see ice on the puddles and I've got my door wide open because it's too hot in here. Burners are a lot healthier than TV as well. Not only does collecting and cutting wood keep me physically fit, but I get a real sense of spiritual well-being out of it.

The council seem unhappy with me housing myself. They'd rather have me living in some sub-standard accommodation for which they're willing to pay an extortionate amount of rent. It seems that poor people aren't allowed to own their own homes without signing themselves into twenty years' bondage. I don't want the council to pay my rent and I certainly don't want the kind of accommodation they'd like to put me in. Instead of praising me for my refusal to claim housing benefit they see me as a nuisance and regularly spend far more than they save by constantly evicting me from places I've no intention of remaining at for very long anyway. They've got it into their heads that I'm some kind of New Age Traveller with absolutely no regard for their laws and institutions. They see me as a threat and pressure me into becoming a burden on the state when all I really am is a poor man who wants to pay his own way in the world.

Gary Brighton

Nicolau Rodriguez

Nicolau Rodriguez

A homely homily

Home is where the heart is?
Maybe I take things too literally but I
reckon my only heart is in my body.
My body, it follows, is my only home.
Do I come across as cynical?
Aw Shucks. It must be that time
of year again. I call 'yet another
day'.

Home sweet home? I wouldn't
call my body sweet but it seems healthy
enough for now. No matter what
anyone sees as their home they've
got to leave it some time, through death
if nothing else, unless ...

Unless there's religion as a comforter
where home will be heaven which
(to ignore the unpleasant option of hell)
given the choice of hell on earth with
heaven for eternity to follow, or just
plain simple life, I have to admit I'd go for
the religious option if I was mug enough
to believe it.

I may seem bitter but having felt that I've had
no home but the body my heart still beats in, still no
matter who or what touches, taints or violates that body,
it is my own. Till death do us part.

Lisa

Aspects of home

Home can be clean and bright
Warm caring on a cold night
The smell of cooking hangs in the air
You can't wait to taste the fayre.

Home can be dark and damp
No warmth no light no lamp
No one to talk to who gives a damn
No one who cares who I am.

Home can be happy without a cloud
Music singing shouting out loud
Discussions decisions lots to do
All part of a family that includes you.

Home can be cold and grey
So all you want to do is run away
Find those things others have
Food, televisions, a Mum and Dad.

Home can be snugly and warm
Lying in bed on a Sunday morn
A place to relax and have fun
Rooms that seem filled with sun.

Home can have parents who fight and shout
They don't care if you're in or out
Buy you anything to keep you sweet
You live your life out in the street.

Home can be a refuge from rain and snow
A place we all love to go
At the end of a busy day
Where our cares are washed away.

Home can be on the street
Our family people that we meet
Shelter a doorway on a cold night
Shouldn't a roof be our right?

Home should be a protection in life's plan
A natural right of a man
Home is where the heart is so the saying goes
Where you happen to be who really knows.

Marilyn Ellar Brown

Home is where I return to myself
Allan Jenkins

It's 4.00 a.m. Nasruddin leaves the tavern and walks the town aimlessly. A policeman stops him. 'Why are you wandering the streets in the middle of the night?' 'Sir,' replies Nasruddin, 'if I knew the answer to that question, I would have been home hours ago!'
From 'Whoever brought me here will have to take me home' by Rumi.
Ela Ciercierska

Cake

It deflated immediately. Not entirely, only inwards from its peak a little, but enough to spoil its momentary perfection. It is deliciously moist in my mouth, subtle in its sweetness, but I think perhaps it needed another two minutes and an extra splash of vanilla.

Washed down with a gulp of coffee. Coffee from my blue mug that I found hanging as always on its hook above the stove. I chipped its rim once running late for an interview. Flung it onto its hook so hard that it knocked against the tiles, banged with an ugly sound.

My eyes meet Jasper's. I know he wants some cake. I know because he has his nose poised high, pulsing as it sniffs. He has no dignity. The cake sits atop a spread of newspapers. One deep drop of icing is smeared across the headlines. Mother will be mad.

When she enters I see her stop and smell the smell that I stopped to smell so many afternoons returning home from school.

Fresh and sweet and warm.

She stops and breathes and in her eyes I see the woman who stooped to kiss hello and listened from the window for our splashing glee carried on the wind from shore. And the wind carried back her call to us and to the house we ran, joined at the gate by our cat who heard her call as his call, and at our ankles trotted. We ran to be scooped within a dry clean towel, and on the table four steaming mugs, one blue.

A lingering smell sometimes oozing to fill every inch of the house, sometimes quivering along the hairs of our nostrils. It was there when the storm lashed the waves to a frenzy and blew sand into Lillian's boots. It was there when spring pushed the first swelling daisy stems upwards through the earth. Now it reeks of a time when sun freckled shoulders ran barefoot on hot asphalt.

The knife dips through the speckled icing and glides deep into the flesh. Mother sinks across from me.

Another steaming mug, and with a hissing sip she splashes back a gulp of the dark delight.

A smear on her chin. A smear on mine. And laughing eyes that dazzled in a summer dress breezing softly around thighs.

Dazzling still. But around the eyes I do not recognise the heavy bones, the slipping skin, the nervous hands.

Conversation creeping over me - not cool and sapping like the teasing tide, but slow, deliberate. I no longer hear the words that tug at my eyelids, gnaw at my concentration.

I drag the newspaper towards me. And sideways from the table's edge I send my splashing mug. I watch the brown fluid spread and seep into the crevices of the tiled floor, as I crouch above a hundred shards of blue.

Barbara Messer

What is home?

Home is where the heart feels at ease. Rooms fill the mind with sense and proportion. Being homeless means one is not at ease. Who is it looking at you as you walk the street? Who's there behind you, stalking your every move, being your shadow? There is no more time for flowers. The streets are your home. You sway wildly as you walk. There is a time for everything but being at home means you rest.

I have a cough, being at home means you get rid of the cough with medicine but in the great outdoors where is the medicine? One can't afford a cup of tea let alone cough mixture. The many men who want you because they think you are easy. You lie next to the trees in communion with nature. The trees one touches as you fall about laughing. Hysteria is being in a library and crying when the book falls flat in your face. Who are you? What are you as you go into a corner smelling sweat because the bath in the hostel has been so crowded, the queue so unbearable, you could not face it.

Homeless is a time for begging the world's pardon, 'Sorry, did you want to say something? Sorry there is something I want to say. Is it true that you kiss babies and make them cry? Is it true that you abused me in my parents' house as they trusted you and you went into a frenzy when I refused and made me homeless so that I would die?'

You know who you are. Do I know who I am? You know what I am now. Disorientated, confused, a woman of no responsibility going into a coma, becoming a full stop. Oh the home I had, the house that Jack built and it fell onto my head crushing me. What is it? Are you now old? You must be at least seventy. You were not the same as a boyfriend, nothing but a would-be rapist out to dehumanise me. The house was no longer safe. It was a prison, it was something I did not want.

House means shelter, house is a dominion of pleasure but reluctantly I said good-bye to my home and wandered like a fool on the street looking at people, being cross and conscious that I was twenty with no money and no job. Confusion in other people's dismay as I ask for direction they turn round, look and turn back. Disorder rules.

If I should die before I write a book I would have lived in vain. Vanity itself is not bad. I pace the floor. I am now warm, no longer angry and it is the past that haunts me, that won't leave me alone. I live there. The past is my new home.

Fatma Durmush

My great aunt's flat before she went into a mental institution
Poppy Villeneuve

A mental institution
Edgar Martins

Home is a cell in a big open plan prison

Homeless people aren't allowed a cell even!
They have to sleep in the
exercise yard! There are people
who get really big cells, with
an unfeasibly big balcony,
perhaps containing a swimming pool, maybe a
garden, a jacuzzi etc. But most people in
this island prison they call the
UK live in approximately the
same sized cell. With a small long balcony
containing a windowbox and no pool.
However the cells
are weird! Cos the
doors lock from the inside!!!
And the screws don't lock you
up at all! Instead what they do is
they skive off driving around in
fast cars & armoured vans not
being community bobbies on the beat.
They don't support measures to get
traffic off the roads (integrated cycle lanes)
thus freeing up more screws to be
Bobby on the Beat. They race
around arresting me for
being a heinous hash dealer - 'soon
he'll be dealing heroin' - Meanwhile
MEAN-fewkin-while everybody else is
locking themselves up at the close of every day like
some great big clockwork orange
while I will get sent to a non-open plan prison for smoking a joint!

Simon Leon Groves

Home not house

Home is where I live. Home is where my wife lives. Home is where our family visits. Our home, like yours, is where we do homely things – watching TV, sleeping, dreaming, waking, cooking, eating and drinking, taking a shower, washing and ironing.

Home is a refuge, a sanctuary, and a place to relax. If you are not feeling well you want to be at home. When the world is against you, you're better off at home. When you don't want to be anywhere, you want to be at home. Home is not just an address – ours isn't even an address.

You can walk from our home to the Piccadilly or Metropolitan line as easily as you can walk to Manchester's Metro. Leeds City station is a stone's throw away, and it is a local bus ride to Liverpool's Lime Street.

Home is on the outskirts of Rugby, and in the middle of Birmingham. From our window we see Lichfield's three spires as clearly as we see London Zoo in Regent's Park. We see and hear a pile driver constructing character-less modern depots in a new town. We view towering warehouses and mills, desolate, disused and derelict now, products of a bygone age. At night we are enveloped in the orange glow of sodium lighting, and are surrounded by an inky blackness, which gives an unrivalled view of stars and constellations light years away.

We live in rural Wales and in England's capital city. We are the only people for miles, and we are two among a million others. Our home is so high that one false step could mean a fall of 80 feet to certain death. It is so low that we can gaze up an airshaft from 50 feet underground to glimpse a hint of daylight.

The postman doesn't deliver to us. Home is in Dewsbury or Devizes. We are anywhere between Wigan and Wolverhampton. Every pub is a 'local'. Our supermarket has no particular name – it is simply the nearest. Strangers from yesterday are our neighbours today. After bidding them 'good morning', we may never see them again.

We have no mains water, gas or electricity. 'Central heating' is a traditional coal fire in the middle of the room. We would never willingly swap our 70 feet of steel for bricks and mortar.

Home is warm and welcoming. Home is a hive of activity yet radiates security, peace and tranquillity, whether in town or country, tunnel or aqueduct. home has no postcode.

Home is a narrowboat.

Andrew Dawes

A cut above
Kees van der Wiele

Mike Seaborne

Coming home

I recently went to the doctor's. I'd not seen the one on duty before. She was a pleasant, pretty young lass. 'Take a seat,' she said, 'what's wrong with you?' 'All the usual, doctor,' I said. 'It's all in the notes.' So she started leafing through my file. Suddenly she stopped, her eyebrows arched in astonishment. 'Wow!' she said. A rather unsettling thing to happen when watching a doctor reading your medical notes, I'm sure you will agree! 'What's up Doc?' I asked, doing my very best Bugs Bunny impression. She turned the file and pushed it across the desk towards me. 'This is your liver report,' she said, and indicated a number with a trembling finger. 'See this figure?' she asked, I gave it an idle glance. 'Yep.' 'That figure,' she said, 'should be between 40 and 60. Your reading is the highest I've heard of.' 'Oh great,' I replied, 'does that mean I should be in the *Guinness Book of Records*?' 'I don't know,' replied the doctor, 'but it certainly means you should be in a wooden box.' 'Well that's better than a cardboard box,' I quipped. 'Don't be flippant,' she said, 'with a reading like that I can't understand how it is that you're alive.' 'Well I don't feel dead doctor,' said I. 'Is there any way to treat this?' 'Very easy,' she said, 'stop drinking!' 'Now who's being flippant?' I asked, 'is there no other alternative?' 'No, the alternative is death!' 'So be it,' I said, 'we're all headed that way anyway, so let's move on!'

Shortly after I left with my usual prescription for the contents of half a small pharmacy. I waited outside for a friend. I could not wait in the waiting room, they have a drinking ban, very sensible in view of some of their clientele.

My friend came out. 'Give me a swig of that!' demanded she who must be obeyed. The dragon is the only person who gets near my bottle! She took a huge slug. Handing the bottle back she said, with a big grin, 'My liver results are in. Guess what I scored?' 'How would I know?' I replied, 'tell me.' '1,954' she said. 'I'm ahead of you by three points,' said I. Poor young doctor, the two worst results she'd seen, one after another.

So it seems we've both nearly served our time in this Vale of Tears, and are racing home. The final hurdle has been cleared. We are neck and neck, with me ahead by a short nose, and Jim is only about half a length behind! Who will get there first? Will St Peter have to carry out a steward's enquiry? Will it be a *dead* heat? At least when I get there two friends will be close! It'll be strange to have a home after all the years of wandering this Vale of Tears! Be gentle with us, Lord, when we arrive. I can assure you we tried our best.

Titanic Barry

A prologue to middle age

To ANYONE whom it may concern, the following is home to thousands of people. It is a home based on a policy of non-discrimination, it caters for both males and females, all ages, races, classes and religions, it doesn't turn its back on those who have nowhere else to go. As an abode it encompasses miles and most people don't even visualise it as a home. For the majority it is just a route to work or a walk to the bank or the shops.

The masses don't see it as a refuge, that tiny piece of pavement, well for them it's just another pace on their frenetic journey to work, another footstep on their way to their home. Well, that pavement is someone's home, someone's sanctuary. Just as your house might offer you escape from the stresses and strains of your daily life, so this piece of pavement procures escape from the disturbing realities of what some child used to call home.

The memories may linger but at least this home will always be there. You see pavement is rock solid, okay it's cold and rough, but it's reliable, it won't reject or abandon you, it doesn't talk back to you, tell you that you're worthless, it doesn't leave you with tainted bruises or acidic reminiscences. So here my roots can at last grow, filter into the cracks and drop deep down into the subterranean, out of sight ... perhaps that's how some people would like me to be ... trouble is, I'm here, and this is my home.

Do I long for a two up two down, central heating and hot water ... no, I long for those corroding memories to dissipate, for someone to accept me, just like the street does. Cold stone doesn't beg a plethora of answers; it just sits and accepts the burden without question.

And how would you feel if some stranger walked into your living room? If they eyed you suspiciously, looked at you in a derogatory tone and then turned on their heels, left your house, your home, without even an acknowledgement? Because you see, when you dance on the street you are dancing in my living room, when you step left and right and walk in giant steps to avoid the cracks, you are walking in my living room. So next time, instead of leaving in such haste, why don't you sit down with me and share the warmth of my dwelling?

Then I could welcome you to a different type of home; I could welcome you to the streets, welcome you to the home that unites thousands of children every year.

Fi Tillman

Visions of home (reality)
Naglaa Walker

Visions of home (fantasy)
Naglaa Walker

Rough rooms

Rough rooms, painted badly to hide the black creeping damp, water drips into electric sockets, and they're fearful to use the lights at night, staircases with broken banisters for little inquisitive heads to fall through, with broken hinged doors and locks that do not lock, and door bells that can't ring as people pound upon the falling front door, needles sprinkled lightly on the bathroom floor, they'd be the only thing to flourish here, walls paper thin you can hear them scream set me free and if they dare to make love we hear every creak and groan sullying something beautiful, for there's nothing beautiful in this rotting place. This is temporary accommodation they were told when their daughter was five years old and now she's eight and still can't read apart from what was written on the hallway condom machine, and when she goes out to play it's on the main road, and it doesn't matter how many times she's told for she has nowhere else to go, and her mother sits solemnly and cries at all the mealy mouthed council lies and a million blue pink green and grey forms she filled in for the sin of being poor – poor translates in their authoritarian heads to stupid but this is not so for if it was she would not cry. In the winter with freezing snow the ice it creaks and cracks the window panes that are covered in brown tape that hides the scenery, but who wishes to look out of them anyway, and in the summer when it burns you cannot open the windows for clean air as they're nailed shut for security. Let's just pray there's not a fire, no exits, fire alarms, or fire escape from this hell-hole hovel of a place. Bed and breakfast is its title but they've gone hungry every morning and their beds are too damp to sleep in so they sleep on the floor and itch all night as something creeps and crawls inside the carpet and these four disintegrating walls. And mother tries to make it bearable with flowers stolen from the park but they just wilt and die in this dark. Nothing can live long here and they have no privacy sharing a bathroom with twenty but at least the toilet flushes well. It did until someone stole the pipes. But at least there's something positive. It means to use the lavatory you must walk down three flights of stairs. It's good exercise especially for children at three at night with no hallway lights. Home should be somewhere safe and secure. Who the hell would choose to live in these four walls?

Fee Jane

Water-lily

My house is full of life. Green things flourish in every quiet room. I love things that grow, the mysterious progress of a seed towards the light is God enough for me. Cathedrals to God or Mammon dissolve when faced with the simple dignity of trees in a wood.

I was forty-five and a veteran of many houses, many lands, many cults and creeds when I first experienced the state of being 'at home'. I knew it instantly and whilst I sat, my mind held still and taut, timeless and blissful in some careful palm, I knew peace. Everything passes, however, and my concentration faded. When I returned to the relative world, peace felt so alien and dangerous that my meditation cushion grew furred with two years of dust while I considered the implications.

I had my own flat by then; the bricks and mortar, the furniture and appliances. I had the mortgage too, paid for by a job where I accepted the grind and the bullying as the price of housing myself.

Who was it that I housed at such a price? Mostly it was the terrified traumatised runaway that was me at fifteen, sleeping rough and gladly, an escapee from my rapist father's fists and my mother's compliant and vicious hatred.

'Run away from home', that phrase always makes me laugh, a bitter snort of cynicism, because I know about us runways. If it had been 'home', a place of safety, acceptance and belonging, none of us would run so desperately, none of us would willingly take our chances on the streets. We flee.

I fled, always looking back at the pursuing demons, the 'home' that nurtured me and which now lodged, unwelcome, in my head. The prime concern of my life after flight was the assiduous and daily bricking-up of those phantoms, the negation of that horrific 'home'. Drugs, booze, religion, conformity, I tried all the band-aids offered in our sophisticated society. Seven years ago it dawned on me that the lodger in my head was a sitting tenant, immune to eviction. I stopped laying bricks, I fell into despair. I spent a month in a locked ward, consumed with terror as the lodger rampaged at will through the house of my head. Powerful drugs numbed me enough to rejoin the world and the doctors waved me off, cured, with exhortations: 'Try to fit in, do what is expected of you, take the drugs and shut up.'

But I discovered something in my terror, something I'd never seen before. I discovered a seed, a tiny part of my mind beneath the fear and the madness that was constant, untouched.

I look ordinary, quite unremarkable. Just another faded woman tending her allotment, unemployed and with few prospects. But inside me, spreading like a glowing carpet of water-lilies across the mere, the slough of despond that is my history, I nurture that seed, that strange bloom of dark and hidden places, home.

E.K.

Within my walls I can dream
Maria Oria

I can only imagine
Maria Oria

Child's fancies on leaving home

Couldn't wait to leave home
to be an independent party
in a place of my own
with my stereo and LPs
my guitar and my books
lots of fit women
lured by my good looks
with my four-poster bed
my antiques and my art
I'd be living in comfort
and far apart
from the meddlesome mother
and the annoying brother
just me and my lover
with a real coal fire
with vintage wine on the rack
a classic car out the back
I'd have landscaped gardens and lawns
where we'd chill out in summer
throw snowballs in winter
glory in flowers in spring
then off in the autumn
to far-away places
until my own private world
will welcome me home.

Charlie H.

Home

Tom stood in the bus shelter, the rain
was coming down in buckets, one nearly
hit a passing cycle courier.

Tom was having a bad day. His
wheelchair bound wife had run away with
a partially sighted knife thrower. His dog hadn't
been seen for weeks. Not even a postcard!
The rain eased off so he plodded on.
'Spare some change please' said a crumpled up
sleeping bag.
'No' shouted Tom, 'I don't give money to
crumpled up sleeping bags' and strolled on.
'Tosser' muttered the sleeping bag, then
settled down to ponder why you can't
rehearse spontaneity.

Tom stood at the junction, sneezed,
covering a Yorkshire rodent in greenery,
receiving a nip on the ankle off
the creature's very vertically challenged owner
in return. So he stood on both of them
and hurried away through the crowd.
He crossed through the park past
'MUGGERS DYKE' but didn't bother stopping
to mug anyone.

He turned onto Unstable Road. He lived
in No. 13. 'HOME AT LAST' he smiled.
The smile was short lived; his house
had been RE-POSSESSED.

Pat

Home is the silence after shutting the door
Angus Boulton

Angus Boulton

Wake up and smell the coffee

Write about home they said,
What does home mean to you?
We'll put you on a coffee table,
What! next to the Danish Blue?

Home is not where the heart is,
Nor where you rest your head.
It isn't where you cook your meals,
Or the place you find your bed.

Home is where you want to be,
Your choice, your life, your right.
Not where you're put for convenience,
Out of mind and out of sight.

Gary Saxton

My home town

I decided to take a trip to my home town to visit old friends, to talk and to stroll around. But on my arrival, I discovered to my dismay a town full of new buildings and friends had moved away.

My home town had changed beyond all recognition and I found myself lost in the crowds and confusion. The town now resembled a block of ugly grey stone. A place I felt a stranger and no longer at home.

Jason Doré

H.O.M.E

H is for the hello, that greets you straight away
O is for the open door, no stranger turned away
M is for me and mine, a feeling of well-being
E is for esteem, a question of self-seeing
The whole is just a four letter word,
Amongst a thousand more
But if you do not have it,
Then you're seen as sad and poor.

Gary Saxton

What is home?

Question: Would I recognise 'home' if it metaphorically jumped up and bit me on the bottom? – That is a difficult thing to answer and would depend (dear reader) on whether I was ready to be 'resettled' into something called 'my new opportunity' having been a spectator in life's rich pattern for the past nearly twenty years. Would the 'cultural shock' to my system be capable of adjusting quickly to even having 'my own front door' and some kind of 'peace and privacy'? I think maybe that question should be posted to that 'great architect in the sky' – a solution truly in the 'lap of the gods'.

Joseph Berryman

The tendrils of the past
Lesley Aggar

Mike Seaborne

The mushroom palace

In a shower of tiny splinters the last tack twists away. We glance back at the neighbouring flats where for the last hour a woman has been standing at her window directly above us doing the washing up, but she sees nothing, her mind is full of dirty dishes. The cold December wind is on our side, sending the broken fence clattering, a cover for the squeal of reluctant nails. We give each other the nod, and carefully lower the pane to the ground. A few deft jerks with a crowbar and the board pops out, leaving us facing into a little square of blackness. I ease myself into the void and flick on the torch. A kitchen, more dirty dishes, sprouting vegetables, pots and pans. The place has been abandoned with an almost indecent haste. I am standing on a fridge, and before I can clamber down it starts humming and vibrating, and I start and send a plate crashing to the kitchen floor. The adrenaline rush is terrific. It seems hard to believe that I am really doing this, that I am actually taking possession of a fifteen-bed mansion, after the weeks in which the seven of us had been squeezed into the two habitable rooms of a derelict terraced house in Camden town, without even any running water.

We explore, padding silently round on fitted carpets, awe-struck. Signs of recent occupation are everywhere; a huge dining table littered with the remains of the final meal, an entire library of children's books. By torch light I find *The Ladybird Book of Home*. Two pictures side by side; one, an empty room, bare boards, a for-sale sign outside the window; two, the same room, furnished, carpeted, a blazing fire, children, a dog. 'An empty house is not a home,' the caption reads. 'People make a house into a home.' I tear out the two pages, and put them in my pocket. For the front door, perhaps, alongside the Section 6. We walk on, through a succession of rooms, little rooms, huge rooms, a bathroom with two baths, beautiful cast-iron fireplaces, hand-painted leaded windows. The house goes on and on, you could lose yourself in a house like this. And everywhere, there are mushrooms, up to five feet tall, in garish reds and yellows. To what end I cannot begin to imagine, but someone, sometime, has used this house as a mushroom factory, filling almost every corner of the house with lurid constructions of wood and metal piping, chicken wire and papier maché.

That first night I spend alone. K heads back to Camden, to give the others the good news, and to dump the incriminating borrowed tools. It is cold, so I position a deck chair in the kitchen, and park myself up in front of the six-ring gas cooker, still connected, and make myself tea. I raid the pantry, and find some salvageable potatoes which I fry up with garlic. My nerves are on edge, and every half hour I can contain myself no longer, and leaping up from my chair I race around the house in wild abandon, like a happy child, laughing at myself, laughing at life. I am just beginning to soak in the reality of it all; tonight I disturb nothing. Alone, I do not wish to attract any attention to myself. I leave untouched the three lights which have been left switched on upstairs. No doubt the council think that this will help deter squatters. The enemy. We are the enemy, and we are here, and the lights are no deterrent, but the warm and welcoming glow of our new home.

Neil Ansell

More home

Just recently, and for the first time in my life, I have found myself attracted to the reality of living in more than one room. Obviously I have always been aware of this as an eventual possibility. I mean, people do that don't they? They have flats, apartments, houses even (although that's just getting a bit silly) ... but not me, never me. But for some reason over the last few months the thought has been condensing in my mind. Taking on solid form as a desire. I'm not just fantasising about it – I kind of want it.

The idea of being able to walk from room to room of my home (of course, in this fantasy I have clean carpets, freshly painted walls and heating). Of having to decide which room to put objects in when I move in. Of having a living room to spend time in before I go to my bed. And, the ultimate fantasy, having another room, a 'spare' room, for storage and to work in. These are things that I would like so much that it makes my chest ache to think about it – so it's always been easier not to think about it. Push it away as a ridiculous day-dream.

Anyway, I feel guilty wanting so much. There are so many people in the world without even one room; and so many people with more rooms than they could ever use, thus keeping them from those who need them. What right have I got to get greedy about space? What right do any of us have to possess more rooms than we can occupy at one time?

But I just can't seem to help myself. I want it.

D–.

Home sickness
Elke Meitzel

A community
Kumiko Okumura

Nests

Crows

Jackdaws

Rooks

Pick twigs

One by one

Carry them high

Up to

The parent tree

To weave a basket

In which to

Place their dreams

What about ...

You ...?

Peter Doyle

No place like hell

Into Crowley's magic,
Tim Leary's as well,
aliens, the occult, acid,
I must be burning in hell.
But better here than the conditioned mind's
cold prison cell.
Here is where the underground hedonists,
the gods and goddesses,
dwell.
Having lost my sense of others' standard,
reality,
I find myself and everything unlimited,
free.
So no great loss,
at least not for me,
I'm staying out of my tree.
(Hee, hee!)

B

Willie in his home in St Lawrence's Square
H stands for happiness, and happiness to you
O stands for old folks and ever true
M stands for mother, you'll find there is no other, no matter where you roam
E stands for everyone and everyone loves home
Sirkka-Liisa Konttinen

Space
Juno Doran

My sky

The sky was so clear, so blue ...
The early morning sun,
the sound of a day to come.
Breathing the cold, polluted London air,
imagining I was breathing the sea.
A beautiful, lonely beach by the sea,
the waves throwing themselves towards me,
as I let them do.
The water singing songs in my heart.
Losing the plot.
Losing the plot to the waves.
Strolling down the streets of London, not noticing the traffic lights, the dog pooh or the screaming school kids fighting past you.
Losing the plot but never really losing it, for it was never there to begin with.
I thought I had it, because you're meant to have it.
Everyone's supposed to have it. Have something.
A plot.
A passion.
Someone to love. Someone that loves you. A home.
Something solid, something untouchable. Something that can't be broken even if the sky fell down and there were only cows left on the planet.
Everyone wants to be someone.
I wish I was happy being no one.
We all have our stories to tell, we all have our skeletons.
I feel like a skeleton.
This feeling, is tranquillising.
It's sadness and emptiness.
Bittersweet.
Worse than losing someone you think you love, worse than the second before you think you'll die, the day you get sacked and your dog gets run over by the milk van.
It's worse because you think you've lost something with feelings attached.
Losing the plot means discovering you've never had it.
You discover your skeletons are as fake as a guy named Zack with greasy, black hair in a wanna-be-bar on a Friday night.
Such an empty feeling.
Under a cold, blue sky it all comes clear.
Let the past disappear.
Let sad things happen, without evil we don't exist.
Where have all the stars gone?
(It's morning now, silly.)
Where are the seconds that'd never fade?
Take a stroll down memory lane.
Write my letters to the people in my life that came and went and stayed.
To the ones who meant something. To the ones I remember. To the plot I never had.
To my home I used to hate. Do not trespass.
Do not park in front of the gate.
Do not fuck with me.
Do not trust me, for I will never trust you.
Don't even try to impress me, for it will never happen.
Then I lost the plot,
and realised the hate was my own fault.
Who said I needed to hate?
Who said I had to blame everything on everyone else and hate every single little lucky bastard on this earth cause I thought my life was so shit?
Home is where my heart is,
and I make who I am myself.
Imagine, something so easy has taken me so long.
Maybe my words just fell
and never made a difference ...

Kristine Lindmark Pedersen

Phoning home

It's time to ring my parents again. This is something I don't often do. I never have anything I really want to say; it's a problem phoning at the right time, as they're about ten hours ahead, and after a while I'm always worried about how I'm going to explain why I haven't rung them for so long, so I put it off for a while longer. However, if there is a time when I always ring them, it's Christmas Eve, so this week it has to be done.

I haven't made up what I'm going to say yet. The truth is out, I can't do anything that wildly outrageous. No, I'm not going to lie, more like colour the sort of truth, make it more pleasing to their ears. You see, my parents are the sort that worry, and I don't see the need to unnecessarily alarm them. Being without a job, much money, a proper home (to them) and becoming pregnant in a foreign country is something they'd worry about. So, I intend to tell them my own alternative version of recent months. Instead of merely relating events, I will express the inner truth of my recent life in a language they are familiar with.

I'm not always able to do this. A few months ago my mother decided to actually come to London. This was about a week after I'd been hit by a car and had taken off from a squat where I wasn't getting on so well, to nowhere in particular. Though I was in another squat by the time I met her, I was still bruised, unwashed and penniless. So I had to come clean with a few things, within reason of course.

But there's no need for that this time so I'm having none of it. I'll tell them I work in a bar, I share a flat with some friends, and that I plan to go to Prague to see relatives early next year which I've been telling them for the past three years.

Actually, I could tell them I'm living in quite a nice house which it is I suppose, even without electricity or hot water, and I'm doing a bit of writing, some of which has been in a magazine. That wouldn't be a technical lie. I don't have to tell them more, as I'd be on the phone too long. Of course if they ask me, I'll just have to lie.

Michelle Arnold

A lottery
Michael Wieloch

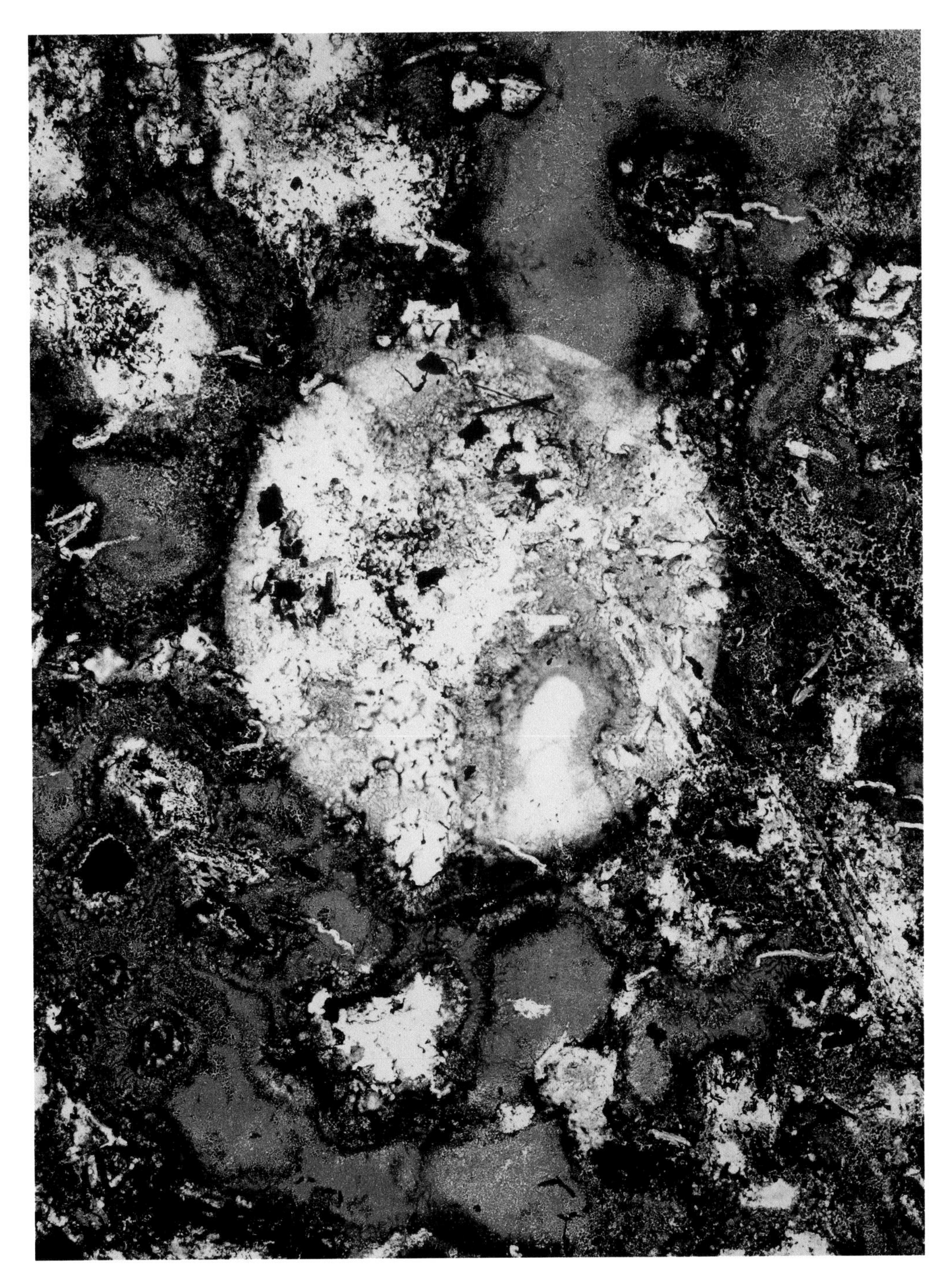

Earth
Before my time
home was not
place was
    everywhere

with I came
dwelling
in dwelling I
    emerge

out of soil
into air
becoming
rootless
drifting
homeless

in dissolution I
    merge
at the end of time
place is
    everywhere
I am called home.

Daro Montag

Hatless

Home.
Is it where the heart is?
Not till I've laid my hat.
Does this mean I won't have a home till I've
got a hat?
My head is quite cold.

What is a home?
A place to stay or the centre of your life.
Is it static or can it move with us?
Could it be where my parents live, that prison
of my childhood? I hope not.
I'm not convinced that it's the house where
I'm staying.
If it is then that's crap.
Could it possibly be within rather than without?
There's one certainty, though I can't be sure.
This planet's all our homes and all our home.
But maybe not for much more.

Simon Mortimer

My four-walled world

In everyone's mind the term home has an individual meaning. In reality it's just a term used by humans to convey something to other humans. To me home is my parents' house in Chesterfield, even though I sit and type this in Dudley. But maybe home is this room, maybe it's this house, maybe it's this town. As the world becomes more global, home is this country and in the future home will be this blue-green planet. I remember my first day at university, the first thing everyone asked me was 'where do you come from?' – basically where is your home? Instead of saying Chesterfield in a hundred years's time, I may say Earth as I arrive at the university of Neptune.

Our home seems important; where we live gives us status. Maybe Mars will become the flat in Belgravia, whilst Pluto will be seen as a run down terrace in Glasgow.

I'm Mr Average, I live in a semi in a respectable area. Should I live in a flat or a terrace in a not so affluent part of town expectations would be different and I might not be sitting here with a degree. Home is a word, but a word of power; it shapes how people treat us. Bricks, mortar, towns, cities, countries and continents are our castle. Some of us are knight templars whilst others are lonely squires, our home tells us our place and our destiny.

Peoples' homes also shape the power they can wield; the Queen is above the law in her palace. The prime minister directs the country from his desirable terrace, while those with no homes fight to even vote. The word home has power and the larger your home the more power you can wield; the bricks and mortar you live in enable you to have more say in the shaping of the country you call home. A home makes you a citizen because you have a mailing address. Words have power, ideas have power, homes have power.

Last of all my home gives me something important, a wall. So when I am king I have something to put you up against.

Michael Wieloch

Sub-terrain
David Cowlard

A suburban dream
Anna Constanza

Before you came

Home is where you come sometimes, and wrap me
in your wonderful strong arms, against your muscled body; hold me while
I free-fall into your warmth and on to sleep. You keep a vigil in your
dreams for me, not releasing me from your protection until morning, when
the world necessarily intrudes.

But though you love and protect my vulnerability
and for that I love you with my precious soul, do not ever forget -
this was home to me
before you came.

Hazel Stewart

Home nightmare

2:00 a.m. on a quiet, dismal, Sunday morning.
In a dimly lit concrete subway the knife slices through
the dirty threadbare blankets like a warm blade through butter.
Searing pain in my arm awakes me from a beautiful dream
returning me to the living nightmare of life on the streets.
In the distance the church clock chimes twice. Suddenly,
my sleepy eyes widen with disbelief and confusion making
my lonely heart beat with fear and apprehension. There in
the graffiti-scrawled and litter-strewn subway stands a stocky
young man glaring over me, flick knife in his hand, malevolence
on his mind. Initially I think my imagination is playing games
with me and my would-be assailant will fade into the shadowy,
early morning gloom, but I'm dreadfully mistaken. I was about to
experience the cold, harsh reality of waking to no home, vulnerable
and alone in one of Britain's cities.

Jason Doré

My house

I get up to a lovely warm house, as Mum and
Dad have been awake for an hour or so.

Breakfast will soon be on the table,
egg, bacon, toast and the usual pot of tea.

After I have left for school and Dad's gone
to work, Mum gets on with her cleaning – laundry,
cooking, what have you, so that by the time
we arrive home again there is a lovely clean
smelling house and the most beautiful aroma
of home cooked food to welcome us.

Dinner over, the washing up done,
we sit down to TV and later we'll have a
mug of tea. At 8.00 it's my bedtime, I wish
Dad good night and kiss him and go upstairs.

Later Mum comes in to tuck me in
and wishes me God bless and pleasant dreams
and switches off the light.

Dick

You and me
Jesus Ubera

1953
Manon Droz

A father's view

To Cal, my daughter, home means her bus or trailer and, most of all, her immediate friends. I am saddened and angered by the way that people, including Cal and her friends, are 'differented' by society. Being 'different' means they become a target for any form of abuse, institutional, personal, or governmental, that is aimed at them. 'They' deserve it, 'they' are not like us, 'they' have no rights, 'they' don't have any sense of responsibility, 'they' do not contribute.

Sorry, but 'they' are like us. Travellers are people like you and me, they have the same worries about life that we have, how to buy food, to keep their homes together, to educate their children and to get health care when they need it. Government has defined them as undeserving brigands and scroungers, the popular press also tells the gullible *Sun* and *Express* readers that they are all thieves and drug addicts! I do not recognise this description. Whenever I have visited a site, Mr IT Consultant in my ultra straight Volvo Estate, I meet ordinary people, who are pleased to see me, to talk to me as an equal and offer food and drink in an open and selfless manner.

I do not sense the community spirit that I see and feel on a traveller site on my cosy Cotswold housing estate. I have only ever been into one neighbour's house in two years, if I was in need of help I don't think I would find any within ten miles of my home if anywhere outside my family. Yet Cal can go from home to home on her site, finding friends and security always and support when needed. So who is right, who has the better sense of HOME, Cal or me?

I write as a fully paid subscriber to the consumer society, a treadmill operative with all the benefits that regular society can offer. I have felt for a long time that we, the conventional homesteaders, have no real answers to our increasing problems. Perhaps we should stop differenting people just to make ourselves feel better, and instead open ourselves up to other ways of seeing, living and doing, we have nothing to lose and could gain a great deal. The problem is, we don't have much time left now.

Marc Buffery

Future home

It's 2010 and world peace is still a distant dream. These are the aspirations for my future home.

In my future home, I will be watching television on a flat screen positioned on the wall. While I'm at work, the solar panels will be charging up the house for electricity.

When I return from work, my wife will be there or still at her place of employment. Having picked up my son from school, we enter through the front door of our house. Resting my feet, I watch him playing with his *Star Wars* Lego. Every time I see him with the Lego, I can still remember doing the same thing in my childhood.

The new electric note-pad edition of the *Auto Express* is placed on the plastic table because I haven't had a chance to read it yet. Walking on the wooden floor, I head for the kitchen. Peeling the potatoes and putting the sausages into the thermal oven, the blue walls are soothing my tired bones. Instead of road rage, the streets are filled with cycle rage. The thermal oven takes heat from the Earth's core.

Parked outside, my Transit MPV is in the driveway. Hydrogen powered, it has more computer chips than my brother's old PC. On the weekends we use it to go to the beach or to the space museum. This is something which I thought would never happen as a head of a family.

Appearing from the kitchen, I see our remote vacuum cleaner passing under my feet. Beeping away, I always know I'm at home when hearing that sound. Looking through the living room, the falling rain drips on the window. However much the rain falls, the purple insulating bricks will always keep us dry and safe.

Beside me, a computer terminal has post and messages. On one message, a colleague at work wants to know where my house is for an upcoming party. Speaking into the computer, I input the directions. Seeing the house in my mind, the bricks and mortar are unique to me.

The opening of the front door means my wife has returned from work. Opening the oven, I see the sausages brown and tasty. As my wife discovers how my son's day has been, I serve up dinner. Placing the food onto the main table, we talk about the day's events whilst eating our dinner.

After dinner, my parents appear on the flat screen by using the Internet. Telling us about life in Australia, we reply by showing a model which my son has made out of Lego.

As the automatic light switches off, I walk up the circular staircase. Saying goodnight to the family dog, the house sleeps until daylight.

Christopher Burns

Other people's lives
Marzena Ostromecka

Marzena Ostromecka

You too can have a Barratt's

Home is where the cupboard's always full, provisions galore
where it's hotter than a vindaloo
when it's Alaska outside
it's near Nirvana, bung a left at contentment
it's a place you can go, where there's no resentment

It's a space without fences
no present past tenses
no regulated gold plated plaques
no polished brass tacks

It's a place to relax and unwind
when you want
feel at ease when you please
if your muscles are tight relax and lay back
then dream on through the night

Then awake all intact
with a smile on your face
'Oh to be, oh to be, back in that old place'
where you don't have to put on a plastic face.

John Fitz

Home is where the heart is

People often say to me I must be mad to live a nomadic lifestyle by choice. It set me thinking just what are the advantages to this way of life, so I started to list them.

Waking up in the morning to the birds' dawn chorus, robins coming into the bender looking for food while I'm still in bed. I've seen kingfishers and herons fishing, otters swimming up and down rivers, hawks catching their prey on the wing, owls hunting at night, salmon leaping a weir, foxes on the prowl at night, badgers playing with cubs in the moonlight, a grass snake shedding its skin. I've seen the most beautiful sunsets over the sea, walked over wonderful moor land, along coastal paths, and many, many more wonderful sights that most people will never ever see.

Of course, there is a downside to living in my home. More and more countryside destroyed by the Human Race. Large tracts of land taken for building development, roads, quarries etc. Rivers and streams polluted, country lanes and hedgerows used as dumping grounds for urban rubbish. All kinds of animals and birds slaughtered on the roads in the quest for more speed.

So, I've got news for you, I'd rather be mad in my home than sane in yours.

John T.

Jim Barron

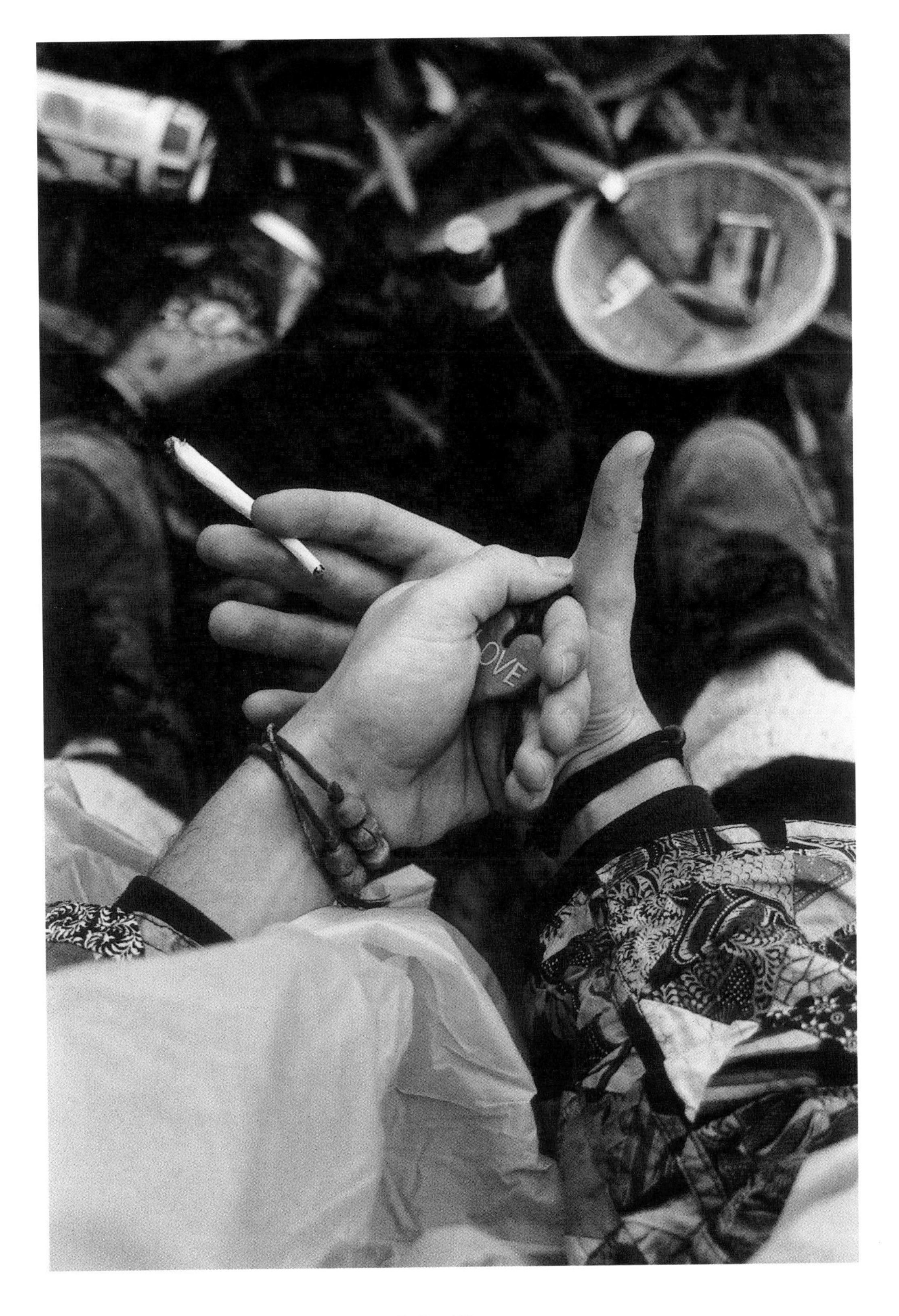

Brian Kirwan

Living in the cold weather shelter

In by six
out by nine
it's raining and cold
but that's fine.

Dodgy food
cold cups of tea
a messy room
with view to the sea.

So called resettlement
with help that's too late
back living on the streets
that's fact, that's fate!

Nicole

Number sixteen

A quiet place
no argument except within myself.

A lovely place
no ugliness except my early morning face.

A calm place
no crying except the wheeling birds outside.

A peaceful place
no violence except on channel four or five.

A beautiful place
no bullying except the puss cat's mild insistence.

A heavenly place
no death except the seasons surely changing.

Christine E. Rowe

Coming home

Home used to be in a drug
Cracking open amps
And watching the white powder
Disappear
As the water from my works
Hit it
In seconds it was drawn up
Then the hit
And I was home.

Garry Orange

Going home

When I get into my car for the drive to Liverpool
I'd get comfy pack the door pocket full of sweets
chocolate covered raisins and chocolate éclairs
it's motorway all the way two hours drive that would be
very boring you might think but for some reason
about half way home I see the first sign that
says Liverpool so many miles then just as I am
getting bored a natural buzz comes over me I feel
like a little kid going on an adventure I haven't
been away that long but I always get this buzz it's
a great exciting feeling that makes me feel so good
I always get that feeling no matter how long
I've been away going home for me is always a
special thing I miss it so much Liverpool's my
home and where I want to be.

Mick Owens

Home to me would be my family,
But people tell me not to be silly.
My friends say stay away,
But I'd like to live my life another way.
Live my life at home,
With my family and my own phone.
Live a life with security,
This is what 'home' means to me.
Alan O'Connor

Going home
Ed Dimsdale

Credits

Special thanks to everyone who has taken part in *The Big Issue Book of Home*, including all those who submitted work that unfortunately we didn't have space for.
Also, thank you to: BA photography students at the *London College of Printing* and the *University of Westminster* – who supplied many of the pictures, the *Trevillion Picture Library* (pages 7, 9 and 103), and *The Museum of London* (pages 79 and 95).

Aggar, Lesley 59, 94
Ansell, Neil 96
Appleby, Kate 11
Arnold, Michelle 105

B 101
Baker, Annabel 55
Baker, Jacqueline-Anne 53
Ball, Len 12
Barron, Jim 122
Barry, Titanic 80
Benedict, Tay 31
Berryman, Joseph 93
Bissessur, Vanessa 10
Boulton, Angus 90, 91
Brighton, Gary 40, 41, 65
Brown, Marilyn Ellar 69
Buffery, Marc 116
Bunney, Tessa 62, 63
Burchill, Julie 8
Burns, Christopher 117

Ciercierska, Ela 71
Claire 21
Constanza, Anna 111
Cowlard, David 110

D–. 97
Dawes, Andrew 77
Dick 113
Dimsdale, Ed 127
Dixon Halsall, Jane 18
Doran/TPL, Juno 103
Doré, Jason 92, 112
Doyle, Peter 100
Droz, Manon 115
Durmush, Fatma 73

E.K. 85
Edsjo, Eva 23
Elliott, Victoria 16
Elvidge/TPL, Arran 9
Ephraums, Eddie 4, 5

Fenton, Stuart 44
Fitz, John 120
Ford, Jacqui 33

Groves, Simon Leon 76

H, Charlie 13, 88
Halliwell, Andy 18
Hannant, Sara 42
Hart, Simon 5

Iroche, Lanre 57

Jane, Fee 32, 84
Jenkins, Allan 70
Ju-Pierre, Jeanette 29

Kent, Steven 61
Kerr, Natasha 51
Kirwan, Brian 123
Konttinen, Sirkka-Liisa 102

Laprade, Bernie 52
Le Ruez, Mark 39
Ledin, Anna 22
Lewis, Anna 17
Lewis, Rebecca 46
Lewis/TPL, Richard 7
Lippiait, Kev 11
Lisa 60, 68

Mahon, Mark 49
Mallett, Peter 35
Marshall, William 14, 15
Martin 13, 25
Martins, Edgar 75
Meitzel, Elke 98
Messer, Barbara 72
Minutillo, Tracey 45
Misé, 11
Montag, Daro 107
Mortimer, Simon 108
Murphy, Alexandra 30

Newman, Lucy 36
Nicole 124
Norman, Jane A 20

O'Connor, Alan 126
Okumura, Kumiko 99
Orange, Garry 125
Oria, Maria 86, 87
Ostromecka, Marzena 118, 119
Owens, Mick 125

Pamela 10
Papandreou, Andreas 58
Park, Christina 12
Pat 24, 89
Pedersen, Kristine Lindmark 104
Peter 64
Pitson, Jo 26
Rainbows Leanne 10
Roddick, Anita 6
Rodriguez, Nicolau 66, 67
Rowe, Christine E. 124
Ruiz, Fabiola 37
Russell, Lucie 3
Rylands, Amanda 27

Sanderson, Andrew 54
Saxton, Gary 92, 93
Seaborne, Mike 79, 95
Sean, Gerry 11
Steph 28
Stewart, Hazel 112
Sunde, Kristin H 56

T, John 121
Tillman, Fi 81
Tommy 48
TPL (Trevillion Picture Library) 7, 9, 103
Turner, Gina 38

Ubera, Jesus 114

Villeneuve, Poppy 74

Walker, Naglaa 82, 83
Wallis, Alec 43
Walshe, Lorraine 19
Watts, Carolyn 34
Wiele, Kees van der 78
Wieloch, Michael 106, 109
Wong, Tony 50

Zadrevetz, Calina 47